OCD: Be Still and Know

A Christian Guide to Overcoming Obsessive Compulsive Disorder

P. A. Kennan

Onwards and Upwards Publishers
Berkeley House, 11 Nightingale Crescent, Leatherhead,
Surrey, KT24 6PD.
www.onwardsandupwards.org

Copyright © P. A. Kennan 2015

The right of P. A. Kennan to be identified as the author of this work has been asserted by the author in accordance with the Copyright, Designs and Patents Act 1988.

Printed in the UK.

ISBN: 978-1-910197-66-0
Typeface: Sabon LT
Graphic design: LM Graphic Design

Contents

Be Still and Know

Introduction

Be still, and know that I am God.

Psalm 46:10

I want to tell you about a healing I received from God on 23rd March, 2013. This event has been so momentous that I can truly say that it has changed my life.

To set the scene: I had just started to be really unwell with a winter's chest infection, and Britain was experiencing its worst cold snap for many years. Temperatures were sub-zero, and where I lived a storm blew for several days. I was struggling to look after my family, keep going and, despite many layers of clothing, to keep warm. I decided to have a soak in a hot bath in an effort to thaw myself out and recharge my batteries.

I had just got out of the bath and was starting to dry myself when I began to cough, a little at first and then a lot! Naked, wet and doubled over, tears streaming down my face, I coughed and coughed; I couldn't stop. The more I coughed, the more I needed to, but it just wasn't working; my throat was constricting. Then, suddenly, I could not breathe! My chest and throat had filled up with something so dense, so solid, that I could not get air into my lungs however hard I tried. I realised that I couldn't breathe out either! Soon I collapsed to the floor, fighting with every bit of fading strength I had left to try to breathe, and panicking. I felt so alone; my family were three floors down and I couldn't reach them or raise their attention. A searing pain burned through my chest and I knew that I was going to die. I remember thinking, "Please God, not like this, not here."

Then, I would not describe it as hearing a voice, but there was a phrase in my head: "Be still, and know that I am God."

I hadn't got anything to lose, so I took a leap of faith and followed that instruction literally. I stopped trying to breathe at all and just lay still on my side. A huge, hard lump of something that tasted disgusting rose up into my mouth. I pulled it out with my fingers and I was breathing again! I crawled out of the bathroom and lay on my bedroom floor shaking and crying for a considerable time, until I was able to eventually dress and go downstairs.

I gave my family an outline of what had happened, but I didn't tell them about how God's words had saved my life. I guess I was too shocked and confused about it, and thought that nobody would believe me. I wasn't sure that even I believed what had happened!

I continued to be very ill for several weeks after this event. In fact, I had never been so ill in my life. Other people I heard of with the same infection had been hospitalised, some of them several times. But it wasn't so much the physical symptoms I had to contend with as the mental struggle. Every day was a real fight against what I can only describe as a 'force of darkness' that wanted to sap me of my life. I frequently felt that I had absolutely nothing left in me to fight it with; I was running on empty. The temptation to just stop trying and give in was almost overwhelming.

What kept me going? My family needed me. Meals had to be made, washing done, the house kept clean for them. These routine, mundane chores made me carry on. Each time I wanted to give up for some reason, thoughts of Christ's temptation in the wilderness[1] came into my mind and the memory of having been saved from death that day. Although the fight was at times nearly unbearable, never again did I find myself unable to breathe, and somehow I knew that it wouldn't happen to me again.

Slowly I recovered, but for many months I found myself going over what had happened to me. Why had I been saved that day? Why was I still here? What was the purpose of my life? It wasn't until towards the end of June that it finally dawned on me that what I had received was an object lesson in fear and how to deal with it. I had been utterly terrified – alone, ill, in a naked, wet, pathetic heap on the floor, struggling to cling on to life. I had called to God for help and He had answered me. I had trusted His words and acted upon them, and I had been saved.

This event and my subsequent illness made me reflect on my life's journey up to that point. I had to acknowledge and face up to what, I hoped, I had always kept well hidden from other people. You see, I suffer from Obsessive Compulsive Disorder (OCD). My whole life, certainly from a very young age, has been dictated by fear. I was constantly at pains to prevent 'bad' things from happening. There were

---

[1] Matthew 4:1-11

so many opportunities for living life to the full that I had missed out on because of fear. There were so many things I couldn't do because I had been too afraid to learn; for example, driving. I believed absolutely that if I learned to drive I would be responsible for causing a fatal accident in the future.

I found myself thinking a lot about fear: What is fear? What is its purpose? How and why does it control us? How can we overcome it? Where do our disturbing, intrusive thoughts come from?

I truly believe that fear is the root of all evil in our world; it certainly has been in my life. Evil is a very emotive word; what I mean by it here is a negative, life-sapping force – something I had experienced so strongly during my illness. It is a force that stops us from living our lives as God intended, that uses fear to control us, paralyses spiritual life, and stops us from doing the right thing. In short, evil destroys life.

My healing that day in March not only saved my life, quite literally, but also led me to write this book, which in itself has been a healing process. What follows is an exploration of fear and how God provides us with the tools to overcome it. I pray that if, like me, you suffer from OCD and anxiety, you too will find healing in these pages.

"It's all about control!"

Part I

A Journey into Fear

CHAPTER ONE

The Structure of Fear

What Is Fear?

1. THE PHYSIOLOGY OF FEAR

Fear is a survival mechanism for our species. Our instinctive alertness to threats provides us with protection from danger and death. The *stress hormones* adrenalin and cortisol surge when we confront a perceived threat, producing the symptoms of being afraid: increased heart rate and breathing, pupil dilation, pain-dampening, a dry mouth, and the ability to advance or retreat quickly. This 'fight or flight' reaction, triggered instant-aneously when we feel threatened, is controlled by a special area in the middle of the brain called the *amygdala.*

Our *genotype* is our genetic inheritance. This has an influence on the sensitivity of the amyg-dala. Our *phenotype* refers to the way in which our individual life experience shapes us and affects what we feel and do. These two,

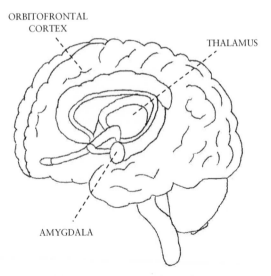

ORBITOFRONTAL CORTEX

THALAMUS

AMYGDALA

Figure 1: Brain Physiology

genotype and phenotype, are interdependent and feed into *neuroplasticity*.

2. THE NEUROLOGY OF FEAR

Put simply, neuroplasticity refers to the way in which the 'wiring' of our brains changes throughout our lives. Nerve cells are constantly creating and destroying connections with each other, as well as adapting the strength and weakness of those connections, in response to internal and external stimuli. An event which has emotional significance for us causes strong cellular connections to be formed in our brains. These cellular networks are the basis of learning and memory.

Therefore, when we find ourselves in what we consider to be a threatening situation, the fight or flight mechanism is triggered and strong neural 'wiring' is formed. Thus, emotional memories focussed on self-protection are created, which we can draw on again and again in the future, along with the feelings which were associated with that particular threat event. These strong, durable cellular connections help to explain why we find it so difficult to let go of the past.

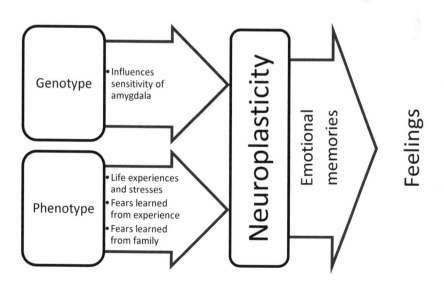

Figure 2: The relationship between genotype, phenotype and neuroplasticity

What Triggers Fear?

There are three basic causes of fear:

- Threat of harm and/or death to ourselves and loved ones.
- Threat of losing our control and ability to achieve desired goals, leading to fear of losing power and prestige.
- Threat to our self-worth, producing fears of being shamed, criticised, disliked, ridiculed, devalued, marginalised, rejected and unwanted.

ANXIETY, OCD AND THEIR LINK TO FEAR

Anxiety: A feeling of dread, fear or apprehension.

Many dictionary definitions describe anxiety as a state of 'uneasiness'. However, for those with anxiety disorders it goes far beyond the mild condition of discomfort which uneasiness suggests. In fact, anxiety is experienced as uncontrolled, unrestrained fear.

OCD: An anxiety disorder in which a person feels compelled to perform certain actions repeatedly to alleviate persistent fears or intrusive thoughts.

NEUROLOGICAL PREDISPOSITION TO ANXIETY

There is considerable scientific evidence to demonstrate that some of us are born predisposed to be anxious. Jerome Kagan, one of the most influential developmental psychologists of the twentieth century, began a longitudinal study in 1989 following hundreds of people from babyhood to adulthood. What he discovered, and other studies have since confirmed, is that anxiety is due to *hyperreactivity* in the amygdala. Such 'high reactive' people are therefore constantly primed for fight or flight; constantly in a threat-responsive state. They show more activity in the right hemisphere of the brain, the half associated with negative thoughts and anxiety, sensitised emotional memory and higher levels of the stress hormones cortisol and norepinephrine. Cortisol levels influence our sensitivity to threats and how we experience them.[2]

---

[2] For more on this see "Understanding the Anxious Mind" by Robin Marantz Henig in The New York Times, 29th September, 2009.

Likewise, scientific research has shown that OCD is linked to a number of neurobiological and genetic factors. It has been suggested that if you have OCD, your brain has difficulty in switching off impulses from a particular circuit. This circuit relays information from the front of the brain (orbitofrontal cortex) to the striatum and thalamus (see figure 1) and also involves the basal ganglia.[3] When the circuit is active it causes you to perform a behaviour in response to an impulse. When you have OCD, your brain finds it difficult to switch off the impulse, even when the appropriate behaviour has been performed.

Imbalances in serotonin have also been linked to OCD. Serotonin is a neurotransmitter that sends messages between brain cells and is partially responsible for regulating anxiety. A key gene involved in this process is hSERT, which is responsible for making the transporter for the serotonin between the brain's nerve cells. For some people with OCD the hSERT works too quickly, collecting the serotonin before it has been able to pass efficiently from one cell to another. Thus messages, or signals, fail to be passed correctly.[4]

So, we have seen that fear is a very necessary tool for self-protection when faced with real, objective threats. However, scientific research evidence suggests that some of us are apparently 'designed' to suffer excessive anxiety. What possible evolutionary purpose can this serve? It is of little comfort to those who suffer anxiety disorders to suggest that society benefits from having such hypervigilant members! It is to the question of how a God-given, protective device becomes subverted into something harmful that I shall now turn.

---

[3] Lewis R. Baxter and colleagues at the University of California at Los Angeles and the University of Alabama were the first to use positron-emission tomography (PET) to study OCD. PET scans produce images of the brain's metabolic activity. Baxter's study, and others', have shown that people with OCD have elevated brain activity in the orbital cortex and basal ganglia.

[4] There is a lot of theoretical debate surrounding the causation of OCD. To date, no single definitive cause has been identified. There are many websites for OCD, but for further information see OCD-UK website, *www.ocduk.org*, which is particularly informative and up-to-date.

CHAPTER TWO

How Fear Controls Us

The fear of man bringeth a snare.

Proverbs 29:25

Fear and a snare is come upon us, desolation and destruction.

Lamentations 3:47

Fear that is a reaction to a clear and present danger that can cause us real harm is what we can term 'good' fear. The reaction is a protective device which enables us to overcome harm. However, fear that cripples holds people in bondage. A fear that causes anguish, paralysis and debilitation is destructive; this is 'bad' fear.

The Bible passages quoted above demonstrate this; a snare being a trap, using wire or cord that pulls tight, and desolation being a state of utter wretchedness and unhappiness. Many people suffering from anxiety disorders are trapped because of fear. They are afraid, both literally and figuratively, to move or take a risk.

The Mechanism Fear Uses

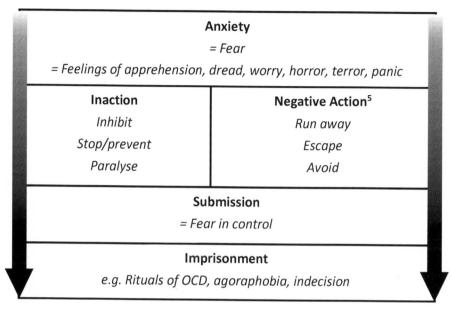

Figure 3: The Mechanism of Fear

Once we conform to the impulses in the 'Inaction' or 'Negative Action' boxes we have submitted to fear. We use phrases such as, "I can't..." "I mustn't..." or, "If I do/don't do this, x, y and z will follow," to justify our behaviour to ourselves and others. Fear is in control of us. Once we have handed over control, it is but a short step to becoming imprisoned by fear.

For example, the second most common obsession for those who have OCD is a fear of harm. This may manifest itself as a fear that doors are not adequately locked or that electrical outlets will cause a fire. So, the person thus affected will experience feelings of worry and dread associated with these issues, especially when they have to leave their house for any length of time or at bedtime. Conforming to the impulse to prevent harm, the sufferer submits by checking all the doors and electrical outlets. Checking once is not enough to be really sure, so

---

[5] I have used 'negative' to acknowledge that whilst this is action, it is not a positive engagement with (or moving towards) something. It is action based on avoidance.

the checking routine must be done several times. But the more someone checks something, the worse their memory gets for whether they have checked! Very quickly they find themselves imprisoned by their checking routines, which could take thirty minutes or more before they can leave the house.

As time goes by, the routines become ever more elaborate and onerous, as the sufferer can never feel completely reassured that checking has been done perfectly. Soon the fearful obsession and the compulsion it generates become debilitating, as routine checking takes longer and longer to complete before the sufferer feels secure, so that even a short trip away from the house has to be planned for. Similarly, the bedtime checking routine snowballs so that the sufferer may not be getting enough sleep as a result. It is a vicious circle as the more the person checks, the more they need to. All the compulsion does is reinforce the fear. Some with this type of fear and obsession will just find it easier not to leave the house. Of course, sometimes they will be forced to do so out of necessity, for example for food shopping; such routine trips thereby becoming another source of huge anxiety. Not only has the OCD sufferer become caught in fear's snare, they also know that their behaviour is not rational and are extremely unhappy as a result. However, they feel powerless to overcome fear's iron grip.

Those who suffer from *social anxiety* have a fear of evaluation and judgement by others. This engenders feelings of apprehension and panic when faced with social situations. Imagining that they will be disliked, ridiculed and rejected, they conform to the negative action impulse to avoid, or even run away from, situations where they have to interact with people. By submitting in this way, they render themselves imprisoned in isolation and loneliness, missing out on so much of the richness of human life. Many of those with anxiety disorders can become paralysed by indecision due to a fear of failure. As they imagine all sorts of scenarios and possible outcomes, making firm decisions becomes impossible.

So we see that *imagined* threats to security and self-worth produce fear (of harm, rejection, failure). By conforming to the impulses of negative action (avoidance) or inaction (prevention, paralysis), submission to and imprisonment by the very fears that those affected sought to avoid is guaranteed! Those obsessed with harm find their compulsions just reinforce that fear. The socially anxious person renders themselves rejected by avoiding social interaction. The indecisive person guarantees their failure by not making effective decisions. Hence, once more, the snare of fear.

But, where do these imaginary threats come from? Why do we believe ourselves to be in a threatening situation?

Fear as a Conditioned Response

Part of the answer can be found in fears and anxieties that are *learned behaviours*. We can control ourselves with fears learned by experience; for example, not putting our hands on something hot because we learn that this will hurt and injure us. Problems come when a fear response becomes paired with a harmless, neutral stimulus. This is what phobias are. Likewise, a fear of something harmless can develop when we witness a traumatic event linked to it. This type of fear generally starts in childhood when we are easily influenced by seeing others, especially our parents, afraid of something. In this case we are being taught to fear; having others' fears imposed upon us. Lastly, others, especially those in positions of authority or who want to be dominant, can control us with fear, usually using threats of punishment to make us conform to their will.

In all these cases of conditioned response we act on impulses of avoidance of a feared object or inhibition of a behaviour. For example, we avoid putting our hands on something hot as the consequence, or punishment, is pain and burning. We might avoid spiders because Mum always screamed when she saw them and got Dad to take them away. Or it might be that we avoid dogs because we were bitten by one as a child; the dog threatened us and it hurt. Maybe we saw a childhood friend choke on a particular type of food, so we have always avoided eating that food. I'm sure we can all recall our parents and school teachers using threats of punishment to inhibit childhood behaviours that they found undesirable! Fear as a conditioned response is therefore a learned sequence of reaction in order to avoid punishment of some sort, generally involving either physical pain or mental anguish.

The same conditioned response is at work with emotional problems we may have. As an example, someone may be unhappy because they are friendless and lonely. In the past they were hurt by a close friend so they have put up a wall of protection to keep themselves from being hurt again; the 'wall' being the avoidance of making friendships. We avoid placing ourselves in a situation which has been painful in the past.

Fear of the Past

Because our emotional memories are focussed on self-protection, it is very easy for past feelings to intrude into the present. We saw in the previous chapter how strong 'wiring' in the brain results from threat events. Now, if the past-learned fear relates to an objective danger, like putting our hand in the fire, all well and good. But not if our fear emanates from an emotional, traumatic event in the past, which is long gone but has led to us developing learned negative thoughts and behaviour patterns.

If we are constantly thinking about and replaying past events, we are also bringing back and reliving all the feelings we had about those events; for example, our feelings of rejection and grief surrounding the break-up of a relationship, or how we felt when someone ridiculed or shamed us. Therefore, if we dwell on the past we will constantly be in a state of grief and rejection, or feeling the hurt of shame and ridicule.

People with OCD often become obsessed by striving to prevent a past trauma from happening again. They become trapped by compulsive, ritualised behaviour designed to prevent the 'punishment' of a reoccurrence of that event.

However, the past is exactly that! It is gone. Time's arrow has only one direction: forwards. If we ruminate on past events, fear of the past becomes fear of the present and the future. By submitting to the impulses of avoidance, inhibition and prevention, we allow fear to control our present and our future life, thereby imprisoning us.

Disturbing Thoughts

Our ability to imagine and fantasise is both a blessing and a curse; the source of human creativity but also of imagined threats. We saw in chapter 1 how those who are neurologically predisposed to be anxious have an overactive threat response. To be anxious is to be in a state of fear, and fear can produce irrational thoughts.

Unwanted, intrusive and disturbing thoughts are very common for those with OCD and anxiety disorders. The obsessions of OCD are recurrent, unwanted thoughts most usually concerned with harm, contamination by germs and viruses, illness, losing control, going mad, making mistakes and forgetting. Cognitive psychologists believe that those with OCD misinterpret these intrusive thoughts as being significant and important. The sufferer then engages in compulsive behaviours to try to resist, block or neutralise them. These behaviours take the form of rituals which can be overt (checking, cleaning, ordering and symmetry, other actions) or mental actions (ritualised use of special words and prayers, counting). Feeling less anxious after performing a compulsion reinforces it. However, as we have seen, these rituals become a trap over time as they need to develop in complexity and frequency before the sufferer feels at peace. This is due to what psychologists term 'thought rebound':[6] the more you try to block out an unwanted thought, the more you experience it. Thought suppression actually increases the frequency of intrusive thoughts and feeds back into the obsession. Avoidance and thought suppression reinforce fear.

At the heart of anxiety is uncertainty about the future. We want to control what is going to happen, so we use our imaginations to create scenarios and possible outcomes. Trying to cover all the bases – "better safe than sorry" – we can imagine all kinds of threats. This, in turn, generates feelings associated with these threats: apprehension, dread, worry, panic. Remember the Bible passage quoted at the beginning of this chapter? This is "desolation". All the imagined scenarios do is create yet another trap of fear: doubt and indecisiveness. In particular, people with OCD believe that their disturbing thoughts have a predictive quality about the future. This is what psychologists call 'thought-action fusion';[7] equating thoughts with reality. Believing that the disturbing thought / imagined threat is dangerous, the OCD sufferer thinks that they have to do something to ensure that the feared thing does not happen, hence seeking safety in the form of compulsions in order to neutralise the threat.

---

[6] Professor Daniel Wegner and colleagues first coined this term (Wegner et al., 1987). Their research has subsequently been confirmed by other researchers.

[7] Thought-action fusion: A thought distortion in which a person equates having a thought with committing an action or believing that a thought is the same thing as reality. See Rachman, S., and Shafran, R., "Cognitive Distortions: Thought-Action Fusion", (University of British Columbia, 1999).

As we have already seen, another source of disturbing thoughts comes from replaying emotional hurts and traumas from the past. Due to that strong neural wiring, we can dwell on negative things about ourselves, thus holding them in our minds and generating negative emotions.

An understanding of how and why we respond to fear in the way we do is the beginning of the healing process. In this chapter I have been exploring how fear becomes subverted from a protective response into a harmful, controlling trap; a trap which causes mental debilitation and great unhappiness, affecting the lives of sufferers and those close to them. Fear is a response to threat, but fear can also create imaginary threats! If we submit to fear, by conforming to impulses based on avoidance, we quickly become imprisoned by it. We learn to be afraid from our life experience but also from the will of others, using fear as a method of control.

Chapter Three

Why Fear Controls Us

The thief cometh not, but for to steal, and to kill, and to destroy.

John 10:10

Fear is the thief that steals our minds, kills our will and destroys life.

Fear controls us because we want to avoid being punished. In the last chapter we saw how fear is a learned sequence of reaction, a conditioned response, in order to avoid either the physical or mental pain of 'punishment'. Punishment – being physical harm, loss of our control and power – attacks our self-worth. Most of us do not enjoy pain, so we conform to impulses that make us avoid it.

For those of us with OCD and anxiety disorders, our minds have been hijacked by fear. We are neurologically predisposed to be vulnerable to its influence. Constantly distracted by imagined threats created by fear, we become locked into an internal battle for control of our minds. Plagued by disturbing, intrusive thoughts which cause mental torment, sufferers become trapped in, and by, their compulsive behaviour as they desperately strive for some sense of peace. But all we find is yet more fear. We feel powerless.

President Franklin D. Roosevelt stated:

> ...*the only thing we have to fear is fear itself – nameless, unreasoning, unjustified terror...*[8]

A major aspect of anxiety is this fear of fear. Fear of our intrusive thoughts leads to anxiety; we become afraid of the feelings associated with fear.

Thought-action fusion theory claims that our thoughts do not equal reality but we can give them a measure of reality in our lives if we act upon them. In thrall to fear, complying with its impulses, our will is sapped and our enjoyment of life is destroyed. Trapped in an endless, debilitating cycle of fear, many become clinically depressed. Indeed, fear can be deadly. In a state of 'fight or flight', too much adrenaline in the body can cause high blood pressure, leading to heart problems. Depression can lead to suicide. Most of our negative emotions come from fear: anger, frustration, hatred, aggression, violence, rage. These can literally lead to the destruction of life. Think of the situations in Syria, Gaza, South Sudan, Iraq and many other regions of the Middle East at the present time and you will see that fear is at the root of all the hatred, atrocities and killing. Each side labels the other as 'the enemy' and unscrupulous politicians and military leaders then use fear to manipulate public opinion to their cause for power.

So what is this thief manifesting itself in our lives as fear? Is it nameless? No! Are we unjustified in our terror of it? No! I think the time has come to name fear for what it is: *fear is evil.* Fear takes us away from God. Think about it; nothing good comes out of this subverted, bad form of fear: hatred, aggression, violence, death and killing, doubt, anxiety, worry. This is because fear does not come from love. The Bible tells us:

> *There is no fear in love; but perfect love casteth out fear: because fear hath torment.*
>
> 1 John 4:18

Fear does not come from God. God's love for us – "perfect love" – removes fear. There can be no fear in perfect love.

---

[8] U.S. President Franklin Delano Roosevelt, First Inaugural Address, 4th March, 1933.

CHAPTER FOUR

Who's Controlling You?

Are You In Control?

You want to be. You believe that you should be. In fact, you have to be in control at all times! It is very important to you that you should have complete and absolute certainty about what is going to happen, and when, and how you can be prepared for any eventuality. I think you're beginning to get a picture of someone, perhaps you, who needs to be *absolutely in control;* someone who measures their self-worth and success in life against this ability.

The fear here is that of losing control, of having no control over your life; specifically, that of failing to manage future events and their outcomes. Your belief is that if you fail in this endeavour, something terrible will happen. We have seen that uncertainty is at the heart of anxiety. In fact, we could call this 'fear of the future'. OCD people, in particular, demand certainty and perfection. They believe that they must accurately predict and manage the future, and that there is a perfect solution to everything. Due to an overactive threat response, the whole of your attention is focussed on the negative, on situations that you think represent danger. If you make even the slightest mistake, the consequences could be catastrophic. You need to know for certain that something bad won't happen. But this is an unrealistic demand because it is not in the power of any of us to know exactly what is going to happen. Intolerance of uncertainty, which is a feature of perfectionism, only leads to anxiety.

> *Which of you by taking thought can add one cubit unto his stature? Take therefore no thought for the morrow: for the morrow shall take thought for the things of itself.*
>
> Matthew 6:27,34

Looking at the passage above, "taking thought" translates as 'being anxious'. A modern reading of this passage is, "Nobody can increase his life by even one hour by being anxious about it. Do not worry about tomorrow; it's time to do that when tomorrow comes." The point here is that worry is of no use. Concentrate on one day at a time. Worrying about the future makes it more difficult to deal with today because your mind is distracted by things which may never happen anyway. Good advice!

At the heart of these fears of the future and losing control is your inflated sense of responsibility. You think that you should avoid having bad thoughts and feelings and believe you have a responsibility to control or get rid of them. Not only this, you believe that you have the power to either cause or prevent bad events, that your intrusive thoughts predict the future; hence performing special ritualised actions in the belief that you alone can prevent harm by what you do or don't do.

It's all about you – *your* attention focussed on *your* intrusive thoughts; *your* belief in *your* power to influence and control future events. You believe absolutely that the future is your responsibility. If things go wrong it will all be your fault. You have increasingly come to inhabit an inward-looking world with you at its centre. Now, this is not to say that you are being selfish. Many of your fears may well be concerned with the welfare of others rather than yourself. The problem is that you must be in control. The irony is that whilst you believe it is within your power and responsibility to control the future, you feel powerless in the face of fear.

Consider the following passage from Jeremiah in which "an expected end" can be read as "hope for the future":

> *For I know the thoughts that I think toward you, saith the LORD, thoughts of peace, and not of evil, to give you an expected end.*
>
> Jeremiah 29:11

Hold this thought in your mind.

Evil Wants to Control You

> *In him was life; and the life was the light of men. And the light shineth in darkness; and the darkness comprehended it not.*

John 1:4-5

In the Bible passage above, John exhorts us to follow Jesus, the source of life and spiritual light; God's Word incarnate. Where there is light, we can see reality and truth.[9] In a state of darkness, an absence of light, we cannot see these things, we cannot comprehend them. We cannot experience God's love for us. "Darkness" is evil. Reality, truth and love do not exist there. However, God's light, His truth, will never be overcome by evil. The light continues to shine, but darkness (evil), a state without light (God), cannot see it because it does not understand or acknowledge it.

We have seen that fear is evil. Fear does not come from love; it does not come from God. Evil uses fear to control us, thereby taking us away from God. This is the purpose of evil. To be in a state of fear, feeling permanently fearful as those with anxiety disorders do, is to be in this state of darkness. When we see through a lens of fear, reality is distorted. When we are motivated by fear, God's love cannot shine through us and be reflected into the world.

The Mechanism Evil Uses

As figure 4 shows, the mechanism evil uses to control us is dependent upon us conforming to impulses of *avoidance;* the threat used being that of pain, as we believe that the consequence of not complying will be punishment in the form of physical or mental pain. It thus relies on our conditioned response to avoid pain.

Imprisoned in this cycle of fear, our perspective on life is distorted. For example, we truly believe that the number of times we wash our hands, or the way we put off a light switch, or position an ornament

---

[9] God's truth: The sum of God's Word is truth. The known will of God is the standard of truth. Jesus personifies, and is the source of, truth because He is the Word become flesh. The Holy Spirit is the Spirit of truth because He guides us into all truth (John 16:13). Truth is reality.
See *www.biblestudytools.com/dictionary* for an extensive examination and analysis of this concept.

will dictate a future event and its outcome. Fear directs the whole way in which we see and hear, and our experience of life is dominated by the demands of our fearful reactions. Fear affects our judgement because when we are afraid, we cannot think rationally. We see threats where none really exist. We go into panic mode and do not see things as they really are.

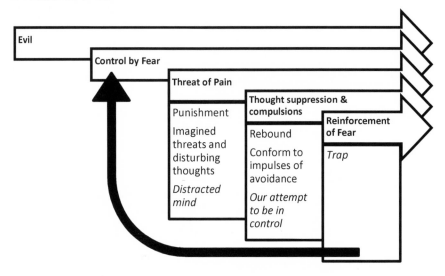

Figure 4: The Fear Spiral

Evil therefore attacks the mind. First, it distracts our minds with threats of pain and punishment in the form of disturbing thoughts. It does this because when we are afraid, we are vulnerable to manipulation and deception. We are persuaded by the lie that we alone have the responsibility, and therefore the power, to control the future. Those of us with OCD and anxiety disorders are neurologically 'wired' to overestimate threat. We are constantly on the lookout for situations that we think are dangerous. Therefore, we are especially vulnerable to this type of mental attack. Next, as we become trapped in the cycle of fear, our will is gradually sapped until it becomes impotent. Our attempts to control the disturbing thoughts merely reinforce the fear. Our problems seem unsolvable and we are convinced of our failure. Finally, we lose hope and evil triumphs. Our disturbing thoughts take us away from God.

In the darkness we are blinded to God's truth, which is love.[10] Acting on the illusion that we are in control, but ironically feeling hopeless, evil uses fear to stop us enjoying life. Fear paralyses; it prevents us from moving forwards in our lives or taking a risk. Evil uses fear to make us question and doubt. It is that nagging voice that whispers, "What if…" "You shouldn't…" "You can't…" So, we don't move; we let fear control us and remain where we are. When we are feeling hopeless, we even question and doubt God's love for us. Fear takes us away from God, away from love. Motivation by fear denies love. All our negative emotions and destruction of life emanate from fear.

Nothing good comes from fear:

Figure 5: The Qualities of Fear

---

[10] See the passage from Jeremiah on p.24.

You can probably add to this list. What is clear is that love does not shine out of any of these things.

Be Still and Know

You are not in control!

You want to be. There are things in life that you believe you must control. But this belief is an illusion. If you take away nothing else from reading this book, be sure of this: *God is in control.*

In the Introduction, I described my own very forceful lesson in realising that God is in control. I had lost control of the very thing that is essential for life – breathing! Hard as I have tried, I don't think I can adequately convey to you just how utterly terrifying it was to know that I could not breathe. For someone with OCD, this was the ultimate lesson in letting go of control! Of course, I now realise that this was the point of my healing. I had to simply trust God, to "be still, and know that [He is] God".

My situation at that point was hopeless. My fight for breath, literally for control of life, was futile. My physical struggle was actually making my chances of survival worse because I was putting my already stressed heart under even more strain. I had to stop fighting and surrender control if I wanted to live.

Isn't this what all of us must do? We need to stop trying to control what only God can control – the future. We have to let go of our illusion of power. We have to give up our need for certainty. It is only by doing these things, by stopping placing ourselves in conflict with God, that we will find the peace we so desperately crave.

> *I am the LORD, and there is none else, there is no God beside me.*
>
> Isaiah 45:5

And yes, we are in conflict with God! By trying to be omniscient, to see into and control the future, we place ourselves in opposition to Him. In effect, we are trying to usurp His power – exactly what evil wants us to do!

This is the crux of the matter. When we try to play God, evil finds a way in. It then controls us with fear, and we allow that fear to be more powerful than God. But all our attempts to be in control don't work. We have seen that they only lead to us feeling even more afraid, powerless and hopeless, and with that we become truly imprisoned.

So, who's controlling you? You have a choice.

Fear is a double-edged sword: both a survival mechanism (a protective response) and a destructive snare. Our fears and anxieties are learned behaviours for self-protection; a conditioned response to avoid pain and danger. However, by conforming to these impulses of avoidance, we can become controlled by fear. We then find ourselves imprisoned by the very anxieties we sought to avoid.

In essence, the struggle is between good and evil. Evil uses fear to take us away from God. It attacks the mind and the will. Fear creates imaginary threats and we respond to threat with fear. So, we become caught in a self-perpetuating cycle. How do we break out?

I think those of us with OCD need to recognise that we are *addicted* to fear. Being permanently fearful defines who we are. We are enslaved by its vicious cycle and find refuge in our compulsions. They become our safe place and we crave them. We crave that sense of peace they provide; initially so easily, and then so elusively. Of course, if we weren't so fearful, we wouldn't need the compulsions! It is very hard to give up an addiction, indeed painful. To let go of something upon which you have been dependent for so long – your whole way of experiencing life – requires a great deal of courage. We also have to learn how to overcome our neurological wiring, our propensity to be always focussed on potential threat and danger.

We have a choice. We can choose to remain where we are, a victim of imaginary threats, following the negative path of fearful darkness. Or, we can dare to step out onto a different path. You can cling on to your illusion of power and remain imprisoned in the cycle of fear. Or, you can reach out towards the light of God's love for you and be released. Because when all seems hopeless, as it was for me, when there is nowhere else left to turn, we turn to God:

> *For I the LORD thy God will hold thy right hand, saying unto thee, Fear not; I will help thee.*
>
> Isaiah 41:13

"It's all about love!"

Part II

A Journey towards God

CHAPTER FIVE

A Guilty Secret

I was in my late teens before I realised that there was a name for how I was; that my behaviour wasn't 'normal'. By chance one day I picked up a page from a newspaper in which there was an article describing OCD. As I read, I realised that this was a description of me. I remember how ashamed and guilty I felt; the knowledge I now had that there was something 'wrong' with me. My OCD started in a very small way at first but snowballed as I grew older, particularly in my teens. It came to dominate my life for nearly fifty years.

As a very young child I was aware of a 'spirit of malevolence' – something that meant me harm. It manifested itself in the form of two 'people'; one male, one female. The male figure used to rise up slowly from the other side of the spare bed in my bedroom. I only ever saw his head and shoulders. His hair was jet black and plastered over his head in an oil-styled fashion; his features were sharp. He would simply stare at me steadily, unblinkingly with glittering eyes and a chilling grimace from which I instinctively recoiled. The female figure I knew as The Butterfly Lady. She was a geisha who sat on a chair by my bed next to my head. She had long, black, fluttering eyelashes, dark hair piled on top of her head, and orange and white wings folded neatly on her back in place of an obi (sash). Now I would describe her as vampiric, then I only knew of her intention to drain me of life, to enfold, consume and suffocate.

Clearly, these 'people' were the product of either nightmare or hallucination, although at the age of three and four they seemed very real to me. Importantly, they introduced me to menace and threat; to a concept of evil. OCD was my attempt to appease this because I was afraid. It took the form of a little rhyme addressed to The Butterfly Lady that I repeated over and over again: "I love you, I love you, I love you." I didn't ever say it out loud though, just in my head and only when I was in the bathroom; it had to be a secret. I now know that this early onset of OCD may have been partly as a result of my being repeatedly ill with throat infections and earache. Studies suggest that strep throat infection, whilst not actually causing OCD, triggers symptoms in children who are genetically predisposed.[11]

As I grew into my teens and adulthood, my obsession centred on preventing 'bad' things from happening (harm coming to loved ones and feared outcomes of situations). If I had an upsetting, intrusive thought whilst performing some task – for example putting a switch on or off, changing a bed, washing myself, writing my homework, cleaning something; it could be anything really – the danger represented by the thought had to be lessened by doing the task over and over again until I felt better. It had to be 'right', perfect. Because this 'worked' the first time (the bad thing didn't happen), whatever it was would then have to be done the same way again in the future. Hence, the many compulsions required a good memory and lots of time! Now my mother knows why I spent so many hours at a time in the bathroom. Yes, routines can develop in complexity into taking hours. This is what OCD does to you. It completely takes over your life, your mind and the way you view the world. OCD comes from fear and feeds fear until you are addicted to it, totally controlled. You are convinced that unless you perform the special rituals, the feared thing will happen and it will all be your fault. When unpleasant events do occur, you blame yourself in retrospect for not having performed your rituals well enough. I firmly believe that this type of life-draining fear is evil.

OCD has been known for over one hundred years; it was first named in the late nineteenth century. Martin Luther, leader of the Protestant Reformation in Europe, John Bunyan, author of 'Pilgrim's Progress', and Charles Darwin were all sufferers. Whilst a number of

---

[11] Research suggests that antibodies produced in response to strep infections, when directed to parts of the brain, might be linked to PANDAS (Paediatric Autoimmune Neuropsychiatric Disorder Associated with Streptococcal Infection). OCD symptoms start within one or two weeks of infection.

theories about potential causes have been developed by scientists,[12] as yet no definitive cause for someone developing OCD has been identified;[13] we simply don't know why some of us are made this way. What we do know is that this is a chronic anxiety condition that causes great distress and suffering, and ruins lives.

OCD is largely a secret, hidden thing because we feel shame and guilt about our behaviour. We are afraid of being labelled as mad and therefore we become adept at hiding it from others; even admitting it to ourselves takes courage. Whilst writing this book, it took me days before I could admit it in writing! Those without OCD find it very hard to understand why those who have it cannot simply exert a bit of will power and 'snap out' of it. Either that, or sufferers are seen as being weak-minded and cowardly, or objects of derision and entertainment on television programmes. Dealing with OCD and anxiety requires kindness and understanding, not least by sufferers themselves!

In the rest of this book I offer a pathway to healing, a way of learning to live with our brain 'wiring' so that we are no longer controlled by fear. The first step is admitting to yourself that you have OCD, that you are deeply unhappy and don't want to be this way anymore. By writing it down, as I have just done here, you are confronted by the irrationality of what you do, how you think. It is out in the open, if only on paper, and this helps to take away the mystique, to break the 'secret'.

We can learn to accept ourselves for who we are, to accept our neurological predisposition without being defined by it. We can change our attitude towards ourself and towards what happens to us. We can be freed; our lives can be changed forever:

> *For God hath not given us the spirit of fear; but of power,*
> *and of love, and of a sound mind.*
>
> 2 Timothy 1:7

We will come to see how God's love for us gives us the power to change, the courage and strength needed to do so, and brings with it control of our minds.

---

[12] See pages 12-13

[13] It is believed that OCD is a result of a combination of either genetic, neurobiological, behavioural, cognitive, or environmental factors. For more on this see OCD-UK website.

In the following five chapters we will find out how to break the cycle of fear and thereby stop being prey to evil.

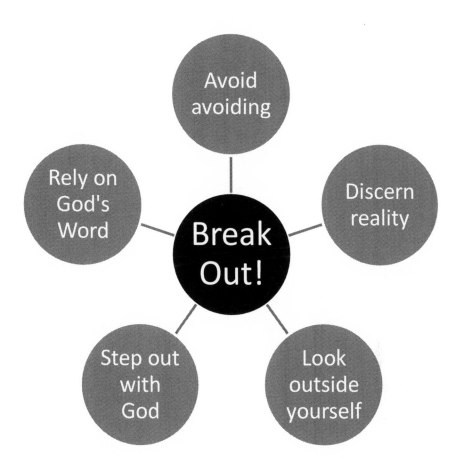

Figure 6: How to Break Out of Prison

CHAPTER SIX

Avoid Avoiding!

Addressing OCD and anxiety problems requires understanding and kindness.

After reading Part 1 you will have gained an understanding of why you behave as you do; an understanding of how and why fear can come to control us. You can now acknowledge the fact that avoidance – the attempt to avoid or escape thoughts and feelings – doesn't work. In chapter 2 we saw that avoidance is the result of conforming to those impulses of inaction (inhibition, prevention, paralysis) or negative action (running away, escaping). The major form of avoidance those with OCD engage in is thought suppression, and it doesn't work! In 1987 Professor Daniel Wegner conducted a study into the effects of thought suppression. He found that trying to forget about a thought, to push it to the back of our mind, makes it come back all the more.[14] This 'rebound' effect is especially noticeable with emotional thoughts and memories,[15] particularly negative intrusive thoughts.[16] We know that submitting to fear in this way, by forms of avoidance, causes anxiety to snowball.

By engaging in avoidance behaviours, fear and (by extension) evil are controlling us. We allow this to happen by choosing to conform to those impulses. We therefore have to *avoid avoiding!*

---

[14] Wegner et al., 1987
[15] Petrie et al., 1998
[16] Trinder and Salkovskis, 1994

So, how do we do this? The flipside of avoidance is acceptance. In psychological terms this means a person's assent to the reality of a situation; tolerating it rather than trying to avoid it. We can start to do this by accepting ourselves for who we are. Learning to feel kindness and compassion towards ourselves is a key step in coping with our anxiety-wired brains. Stop giving yourself such a hard time with guilt, shame and blame! Stop punishing yourself by thinking that you are abnormal, weird, or weak for feeling fearful. All that self-criticism only increases your anxiety. If we can self-accept, anxiety will reduce.

Now, acceptance doesn't mean throwing your hands up in defeat and resignation to your neurological wiring. Nor does it mean seeing yourself as a victim, defined by your anxiety condition. Acceptance means seeing yourself realistically; recognising your predisposition toward anxiety, but learning how to live with it so that it doesn't control you. After all, we are as God made us and we cannot change that.

However, you can learn to manage your anxiety-wired brain. For example, I find that OCD becomes much worse at times of stress. At such times, when you feel the urge to conform to fearful impulses, keep that phrase, "The fear of man bringeth a snare," or, "Fear is a trap," in mind. By doing this, you can resist the urge to compulsive avoidance behaviours because you know they will only make your anxiety worse. Just take pause ("Be still, and know that I am God"), acknowledge that fear is a trap (evil trying to control you), that compulsive behaviour won't help you – and the fearful thought passes. Doing this every time you feel afraid soon results in having fewer intrusive thoughts, generally feeling calmer and less anxious. It takes practice, but the more you do it, the easier it becomes.

You might say that keeping these phrases in mind is in itself a compulsive behaviour, a form of thought suppression. Well, to a point it is. The difference is that you are not trying to run away from the fearful thoughts and feelings. In fact, you are accepting them, tolerating them until they pass. You are countering them with the understanding and knowledge that irrational, ritualised behaviours are a trap – one that only leads to more fear.

Tolerating fear and anxiety will lead to feeling less anxious. This type of self-acceptance needs to be nurtured over time. Eventually you will find that rather than simply tolerating fearful feelings, you can allow these feelings to come and go without experiencing any anxiety. You will be able to be with the feeling rather than wanting to run away from it.

In the following two chapters I will be exploring other aspects of acceptance. For now, it is just important to recognise that knowledge and understanding of your anxiety condition and behaviour can help to bring self-acceptance. Knowledge and understanding prevent us from entering into a state of blind panic and irrational fear. Remember, God did not give us the spirit of fear but of power. Understanding gives us the power to counteract fear. God's love for us, revealed in His Word and guidance, gives us the strength of will and mind, the courage, needed to resist fear and evil. It is only by struggling with something in life that we find difficult, whatever it might be, that we learn, grow spiritually and in doing so are able to overcome.

CHAPTER SEVEN

Discern Reality

Forget about the fear, focus on the reality.[17]

Chris Hadfield, the "Singing Astronaut", when being interviewed about the 240 days he spent working on the International Space Station, said that this was how he coped when having to work alone in the vastness of space. Concentrating on what is in front of you right now, not on what you can't see or what you imagine, is a very good tool for dealing with fearfulness.

In many respects this approach is what Buddhists refer to as mindfulness.[18] This mental discipline entails learning how to pay active, open attention in the present moment without making any evaluation or judgement. You direct your attention to only observe your feelings and thoughts without judging them to be good or bad. It is very much about being in the now, not the past (remembering) or projection into the future (imagining). After all, the present is the only reality; not the past, that's gone, and not the future because it may never happen.

Is the Threat Real?

When you feel afraid you are reacting to a perceived threat. It is important to discern if that threat has any basis in reality right now. Can you see it, or are you imagining it? I can guarantee that if you have

---

[17] "Stargazing Live", BBC2, 8th January, 2014.
[18] For more on this see *bemindful.co.uk*. There are also several online tutorials for this technique.

OCD, most of what you believe to be threatening is not real. It might have been in the past, it could be in the future, but not right here, right now in front of you! Remember, if you are seeing the world through a lens of fear, reality is being distorted; scared people are easy to manipulate when their minds are under attack from fear. Having an awareness that you are being controlled in this way can help you to reject the trap of your compulsions. Therefore, vigilance is required! Don't give those disturbing thoughts and imaginary fears a reality by acting on them. If you do not want to be trapped in the cycle of fear, you have to act against fear and compulsion persistently. Go through your steps: take pause; observe the disturbing thought in the now (no remembering or imagining); and refuse to be trapped, reject the fear.

> *God hath not given us the spirit of fear; but of power ... and of a sound mind.*
>
> 2 Timothy 1:7

Is the Past Real?

Take some time to consider this question. The Oxford English Dictionary defines 'reality' as:

> *The state of things as they actually exist; the state or quality of having existence or substance.*

Does the past exist for you? Does it have an objective reality? I came to realise that, for me, the past was just as real as the present. I was constantly replaying it in my mind, especially traumatic events that had made me fearful, thereby giving it an existence in the present. Is it like this for you?

We have to stop replaying the past. Stop dwelling on it right now! By replaying, you are reliving the fearful feelings and keeping them alive. You are giving power to past events and traumas so that they poison the present. We have to accept that the past is gone, that it no longer exists and therefore it does not have a reality in our lives now. However much you dwell on it, you cannot control the past because you cannot change what has happened. It is therefore pointless and futile to keep going over and over it. All you are doing is punishing yourself and preventing your enjoyment of life now.

Albert Ellis, an American psychotherapist and psychologist, published a series of articles in 1957 which established a form of cognitive therapy known as Rational Emotive Behaviour Therapy (REBT).[19] This posits that your feelings and reactions are generated by your thoughts not by events. We cannot blame past events for being the cause of our fears and anxieties in the present. Rather, it is how we view unpleasant events, our interpretation of what happens to us, that influences our feelings. Are we holding on to negative thoughts, self-defeating or irrational beliefs? For example, self-blame, self-pity, anger, guilt, shame, hurt, fear and anxiety? By dwelling on the past we immerse ourselves in this negativity. REBT is based on the idea that if you change how you think, you can change what you feel.

We do have a choice over how we view traumatic or unpleasant events. We do have the power to change our attitude towards them. For example, by not 'awful-izing'. This means not using phrases such as, "It was terrible;" "It was awful;" "It was a disaster, a catastrophe;" etc. to describe to ourselves, in our interior monologues, how we felt about an event. Such language only makes something seem more frightening. Likewise, we can ameliorate our intolerance of such events by not using phrases such as, "I hate..." "I can't bear..." "It's unbearable."

Just as we need to learn self-acceptance, we also have to learn how to life-accept. Changing what you can – your attitude and thought about events – helps you to live with what you can't change – past traumas and your anxiety-wired brain.

The Bible tells us:

> *Remember not the former things, nor consider the things of old. Behold I am doing a new thing; now it springs forth, do you not perceive it?*
>
> Isaiah 43:18-19 (RSV)

Concentrate on the now, start anew, and allow the past to die.

The Torment of Fear

> *...fear hath torment.*
>
> 1 John 4:18

---

[19] Ellis, Albert, "Rational Psychotherapy and Individual Psychology", Journal of Individual Psychology 13: 38-44, (1957). Ellis, Albert, "Reason and Emotion in Psychotherapy", (Stuart, New York, 1962)

Have you noticed how your disturbing, intrusive thoughts focus on the very worst things that could happen; disaster being the only possible outcome? No wonder we are afraid of these thoughts! But this torment is not based on reality. Whatever the feared thing is, it does not exist now. These thoughts are just that: thoughts, ideas, imaginings; they have no concrete, objective reality. Have you ever stopped to question why you, in particular, should have been singled out and endowed with supernatural, predictive powers? Remember where this type of tormenting fear comes from! By trying to be all-seeing, all-powerful, in control, we place ourselves in opposition to God. Refuse to be trapped; reject the fear.

> *For I know the plans I have for you, says the LORD, plans for welfare and not for evil, to give you a future and a hope.*[20]
>
> Jeremiah 29:11 (RSV)

Perfectionism demands certainty. Those of us with OCD are overwhelmingly perfectionists; we cannot bear the uncertainty of not knowing what is going to happen. But perfectionism is unrealistic. Our reality is uncertainty. Why? Because it is inherently impossible to accurately predict something which has no reality. You cannot alter something which may never happen! Part of life-acceptance – changing what you can and living with what you can't – has therefore to be an acceptance of uncertainty. There will be no fear of what is to come if you can accept that you do not have the power to control the future. What you *do* have the power to do is to change your mental attitude. Making plans for the future based on solid evidence in the now (tormenting fears do not fulfil this criteria!) is all that you can do.

Make a commitment to yourself that from now on you will only deal with what is real, now, today! Forget the illusory fears that come from darkness. Their only purpose is to torment and torture you, to stop you from enjoying life. Accept that the past and the future have no reality and that, therefore, you cannot control them. For how can you control something that does not exist?

---

[20] Previously quoted in chapter 4, but the RSV translation has been used because 'thoughts' are replaced by 'plans' which brings another dimension to this verse, especially here when considering fear of the future.

When fear assails you and threatens to overwhelm, follow these steps:

- Take pause. ("Be still, and know that I am God.")
- Discern what is real. (Is there a danger in front of you now?)
- Know that fear does not come from God. ("For God hath not given us the spirit of fear...")
- Reject the fear, forget it.
- Refuse to be trapped; avoid avoiding.

Acting persistently against fear in this way will free you from the addiction of your compulsions and will release your mind from the control of darkness.

> *For God hath not given us the spirit of fear; but of power ...*
> *and of a sound mind.*
>
> 2 Timothy 1:7

CHAPTER EIGHT

Look Outside of Yourself

Set your affection on things above, not on things on the earth.

Colossians 3:2

Let your whole mind and thought be set on the spiritual, not on the material things of this world. A literal reading of this means not being so concerned with the acquisition and retention of wealth and material possessions. But it can also be taken to mean not being so focussed on our personal sense of power and control, or being so fearful of what others can do to us.

OCD is very much about a fear of what the future will bring. It is about having an overwhelming need to prevent bad events from happening. The previous chapter considered why this need for control is so unrealistic. Another aspect of acceptance is acknowledging that 'bad' or undesirable things will happen to us, regardless of what we do or don't do. However, we can control our attitude towards what life throws at us. Our attitude does not have to be a fearful one!

Viktor Frankl, a Viennese neurologist and psychotherapist, was interned in a Nazi concentration camp from 1942-1945. This experience led to his developing a type of therapy known as logotherapy;[21] the underlying theory of which concerns making meaning out of whatever circumstances we find ourselves in. Whilst we cannot control what happens to us, we can choose the attitude we take

---

[21] Frankl, Viktor, "Man's Search for Meaning", (Beacon Press, Boston, 2006)

towards these events, ourselves and the conditions we face. If we can learn to identify positive meaning in whatever comes our way in life, we will be empowered rather than assigning ourselves as victims of our circumstances.

Thus, we can be wired for anxiety, wired for OCD, but we do not have to be defined by our brain state, a victim of it. Of course, we can't control our physiology, but we can alter our subjective experience of it and our behaviour. In other words, do we have to fear the fear? Do we have to interpret our thoughts in a negative way, always expecting the worst and experiencing constant dread and foreboding as a result? Do we have to give in to our compulsions? No! These are the areas over which we do have power and control.

Taking a spiritual viewpoint, God has a plan for each and every one of us. Remember Jeremiah 29:11; our life events happen specifically to each of us for a reason. They are given to us to help us learn and grow, not to make us run away and withdraw from life. (We know what happens if we follow that path of avoidance!) Our life events are points along our spiritual journey, taking us closer towards God. This can be hard to see or appreciate when you are in the midst of something stressful or traumatic. But if we can take something positive out of whatever happens along that journey, evil will have no power over us.

We saw in chapter 4 how fear makes us insular. We can become so focussed on our thoughts, our feelings, that we become lost in an interior darkness. So convinced are we of our responsibility to be in control, of our power to influence events, that the dictatorship of fear stops us from engaging with life.

Here's a useful analogy: you know how when you are ill or in pain that the illness/pain absorbs you entirely and becomes your whole focus? The reason is that you are afraid of it. Evil – that force for negativity – uses fear in exactly the same way so that we become completely locked into it. How can you counteract this? Look outside yourself! How can you use your life in a positive way? For example, think of what you can do to help others. In what ways could you offer your life experiences back to the world? Doing something constructive with your life in this way will divert your attention away from your fears and you will gain an entirely new perspective on life – one that is positive, no longer self-centred but outward-looking, engaging, giving and joyful. You will be *in* life instead of *out* of it. Go on, lose yourself!

> *The LORD is on my side; I will not fear: what can man do unto me?*
>
> Psalm 118:6

Many of our fears are often about what we believe others can do to us. These can range from threats of physical violence and harm, to being thwarted in our desires, goals and aims, through to perceived threats to our self-worth. At the heart of such fears is our anticipation of losing power and control over our lives; of having someone else's will imposed upon us. But these fears result from wrong thinking on so many levels. We've already seen how anticipation, projection and imagination lead to unreal fears. Know this: there is only God's will at work in our lives; not your will, mine or anyone else's. Of course, many of us expend a great deal of time and effort in the futile attempt to assert our will, to be in control, ultimately seeking to have our own way. See how we become engrossed by 'things of the earth', the material concerns of the world? But in the end, as Jesus confirmed:

> *...not my will, but thine, be done.*
>
> Luke 22:42

God has all power. So, what can anyone else do to us? Man is not more powerful than God. Therefore, we need not feel any fear towards others.

Just as our sense of power and control is illusory, so is fear.

CHAPTER NINE

Step Out with God

Be strong and of a good courage; be not afraid, neither be thou dismayed: for the LORD thy God is with thee withersoever thou goest.

Joshua 1:9

Courage

I'm sure that many of you, if you've read this far, will be thinking to yourselves, "She makes it sound so easy – 'avoid avoiding, act persistently against fear, change your attitude, step out with God' – but I'm not ready for this yet. I'd rather stick with what I know, what I'm comfortable with. I can't make these changes. I'm too afraid!"

Don't panic! I do know how you feel because I've gone through it too. Changing your whole way of thinking and behaving, your attitude towards yourself and life, does require courage. For many of you, like me, this might mean trying to undo a lifetime's patterns of behaviour. It isn't easy, there will be times when you falter, but we are not alone! You don't have to go through this on your own:

For I the LORD thy God will hold thy right hand, saying unto thee, Fear not; I will help thee.

Isaiah 41:13

Overcoming fear requires courage: the ability to act in spite of your fear. But remember, God did not give us this spirit of fear. Instead, God's gift of His Holy Spirit, which comes to those who believe, gives power to all who need it to do what He asks of them. This gift provides us with the strength, the courage and confidence we need to confront fear. And this courage brings with it control of our minds.

You are going to need to draw on this courage time and again as you go through the process of giving up your addiction to fear and breaking out of the trap. Perhaps the greatest amount of courage is needed just to admit to yourself that you have a problem which is distorting your life – the realisation, followed by acceptance, that your life does not have to be this way. Changing your attitude to one of acceptance – of yourself, of uncertainty (giving up the need for control), being prepared to tolerate fear and anxiety, and always looking for positivity wherever you are – requires courage. Making a commitment to persistently act against fear and anxiety, by mentally rejecting it, needs a great strength of will. As does resisting the impulse to submit to fear, and denying your desire for compulsive and avoidance behaviours; rejecting your fearful and disturbing thoughts for the illusions that they are; rejecting a fear of what you believe others can do to you, and attempts by others to foist their fears on you.

You will need to be very strong in your determination to achieve these things; to overcome the fear of giving up the safety of your rituals. But it is all possible if you will accept God's help. Will you listen to God? Will you accept His help? Stepping out with God means moving out on to a new path, a new way of living and seeing, where there is no more fear. You are freed forever because you are no longer vulnerable to manipulation by fear and evil. Why? *Because God loves you.*

When you listen to God and know and accept His love in your life, the illusion of fear created by evil melts away. You see it for the sham that it is. You stop allowing fear to be in control of your life. You stop allowing fear to be more powerful than God.

Love

> ...*love comes from God. Whoever loves is a child of God and knows God. Whoever does not love does not know God, for God is love.*
>
> 1 John 4:7-8 (GNB)

God is love and God loves us.

Yes, that's right! God loves you! Why do so many of us find this so hard to accept? God's love is there for us always; His help is readily available. It is we who must open ourselves up to this love and be prepared to receive it. Because when we turn to God for help there is comfort and support.

> *God is love, and whoever lives in love lives in union with God and God lives in union with him. Love is made perfect in us in order that we may have courage ... There is no fear in love; perfect love drives out all fear.*
>
> 1 John 4:16-18 (GNB)

As we know, fear has to do with the future, the unknown. When we open ourselves up to God's love, we can be totally confident in the knowledge that these things are under God's control. His perfect love thus removes fear and brings hope, courage and confidence, and along with these the peace we so desperately crave. We find our refuge in God's love for us, not in the compulsive rituals of fear.

It is we who give permission to fear to be more powerful than God in our lives. When we acknowledge God's love for us, when we listen to and receive His Word, the balance of power shifts. Remember the fear list in chapter 4? Now compare it with all the positive attributes that emanate from love (see figure 7 overleaf).

When we are no longer motivated by fear but instead act from and within love, all these good things will come to us. Unlike fear, love does not seek to imprison and control. Instead, God's love frees us for a new life.

> *And ye shall know the truth, and the truth shall make you free.*
>
> John 8:32

And what is that truth? *God's love.* This is reality. When we live in the light of this love, all our fears are left behind. Our lives are transformed. Why? Because nothing can separate us from the love of God.

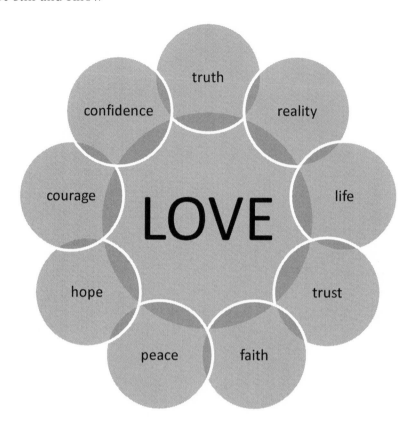

Figure 7: The Qualities of Love

Who shall separate us from the love of Christ? Shall tribulation, or distress, or persecution, or famine, or nakedness, or peril, or sword?

Romans 8:35

We can face the future fearing no evil because God is on our side. God's love withholds nothing from us. God showed (and shows) us His love in giving His own son, Jesus Christ. Christ's life, death and resurrection, and the gift of the Holy Spirit – 'the Comforter'[22] – prove God's everlasting love and omnipotence. Neither suffering, nor death, nor any power can part us from the divine love.

---

[22] See John 14:16,26

...in all these things we are more than conquerors through him that loved us. ... neither death, nor life ... nor powers, nor things present, nor things to come, ... nor any other creature, shall be able to separate us from the love of God, which is in Christ Jesus our Lord.

Romans 8:37-39

God's love is with us always and it is this which brings us peace:

Let not your heart be troubled, neither let it be afraid.

John 14:27

Trust

Of course, in the end it all comes down to trust. We overcome fear by trusting God.

What does this mean? Having a firm belief in God's omnipotence and love. Accepting these as the only reality. Relying on God in our daily lives, because we believe in the ability, reliability and strength of God's power and love which bring hope and confidence.

It is better to trust in the LORD than to put confidence in man.

Psalm 118:8

The known will of God is revealed to us in the Bible. Remember that passage from Jeremiah 29:11? God wants to free us from fear. Look back at 2 Timothy 1:7. God saves us from fear. When we trust Him, we can have a life without it. I know this! When I turned to God for help, and I believed and trusted, I was healed. You can be too.

If you want to beat your addiction to fear, you have to trust God. Because when we submit to fear, when we feel permanently afraid, we are not trusting Him. Conversely, when we respond to God by having confidence in His promises, knowing that He will help us, that the future is in His control, that He is with us, our fears disappear. By stepping out with God we place our trust in His faithfulness. So, you have the choice: step out or stay where you are. But once you accept God's invitation, there's no looking back! You can leave your old life behind.

Be Still and Know

Meditation

When you're feeling afraid, stressed, overwhelmed, read or say this slowly focussing on the underlined words.

> *Be still, and know that I <u>am</u> God.*
>
> Psalm 46:10

> *Be still, and <u>know</u> that I <u>am</u> God*
> *Be still, let go and <u>know</u> that I <u>am</u> God*
> *Be still, let go and <u>know</u> that I <u>am</u> love, I <u>am</u> God*
> *Let go and know.*

CHAPTER TEN

Rely on God's Word

...for without me ye can do nothing.

John 15:5

Therapy?

The usual treatment offered to those who have anxiety disorders, including OCD, is cognitive behavioural therapy (CBT). This is a psychological therapy which claims to help people change their thinking, confront their fears and alter their behaviour patterns.[23] Whilst I do not seek to devalue these aims, CBT has been widely criticised by both service users and providers.[24] Its efficacy has been called into question on a number of points: it is only a short-term intervention; it has a goal-oriented, 'one size fits all' approach which does not take into account individual differences and needs. CBT is therefore suitable for some people, but not all. Many of those who have undergone a course of CBT regard it as having been cold, uncaring,

---

[23] Cognitive therapy was first developed by Albert Ellis as REBT (see note 18, chapter 7). CBT, a combination of cognitive and behavioural therapies, was developed out of Ellis' work by Professor Aaron Beck, and others, from the 1970s onwards. CBT is based on the understanding that it is thoughts and feelings that influence behaviours.

[24] See Rowe, Dr. Dorothy, "Cognitive behavioural therapy – no more than another Labour quick-fix", psychminded.co.uk, 9th October, 2008 and Hussain, Angela, "CBT 'does not work' says second high-profile clinical psychologist", psychminded.co.uk, 20th March, 2009. Both articles are followed by discussions and testimonies from both psychologists and patients.

lacking in compassion and understanding, simplistic, inadequate, taking a 'pull yourself together' approach which has actually led them to become more depressed!

Many psychologists are also critical of its use and efficacy. For example, Dr Oliver James has gone as far as to state:

> *The fact is, it doesn't work ... After 18 months, those given CBT have no better mental health than ones who have been untreated.*[25]

He is not alone. A review of 175 trials in the British Journal of Psychiatry concluded that the effects of CBT are exaggerated: 67% improved with CBT, but 40% improved without it.[26] Another review, conducted by Professor Drew Weston, found that two years after treatment 66% of people had relapsed or needed further help.[27]

Why is CBT so ineffective? Because, as is common with many medical treatments and therapies, it treats a person's symptoms but not the cause of their problem. In other words, it does not address the root of their anxiety. CBT may offer someone a degree of insight, but it does not eradicate their problem in the long-term.

Healing

True healing comes from God. Apart from God we can do nothing.

The trouble with CBT and other forms of therapy is that they ignore our spiritual being and wellbeing. They leave God out of the picture entirely! No wonder they have such limited success.

Fear emanates from denying God in your life. We put ourselves apart from God by not trusting Him, not believing in His omnipotence, by trying to control what is not in our power to control. This is how we become prey to evil, when we are apart from God. This is the real root of your anxiety.

When you have OCD, feelings of dread and even terror overwhelm and control you, and there is always something you are afraid of. However, even when the threat is real, the fear we feel is not; it is an

---

[25] See article by Angela Hussain, referenced in note 24

[26] Quoted in The Independent, 23rd March, 2010, by Jeremy Laurance in his article, "The Big Question: Does Cognitive Therapy Work and Should the NHS Provide More Of It for Depression?"

[27] See Weston, Professor D., et al., Psychological Bulletin, (2004), (130, 631 663)

illusion. We project; we imagine consequences and outcomes of events which may never happen. Added to this, especially for those who have OCD, we take on personal responsibility for everything that happens, or may happen in the future. All this does is generate more feelings of fear and terror. When you have OCD, you then give in to your compulsive rituals in an attempt to run away from these feelings, to quell them and find some peace. Of course, in this way the cycle of fear starts all over again. Always being terrified like this is not a life! This is the dictatorship of fear.

Fear is a bully. How do we overcome bullies? By confronting them, standing up to them.

> *I will say of the LORD, He is my refuge and my fortress: my God; in him will I trust.*
>
> Psalm 91:2

By taking your refuge in God you can stand up to fear and overcome it because you know that you are not alone; God is with you. We acquire strength of mind and will by giving up our need to be in control. By accepting God's omnipotence we give control back to Him, where it belongs, and thereby relieve ourselves of always feeling responsible. We can then accept that, however hard we try to, we cannot truly control the actions of others or influence events which have not yet happened. By trusting in God's love, in God's plans for welfare and not for evil, we are freed from fear.

Unlike therapy, God's love for you is not a short-term treatment; it is always there. Added to this, God's healing love is tailored to each person's needs.

Turn to the Bible

I never cease to be amazed by God's healing Word. You will have noticed that through the course of this book I have been frequently quoting from the Bible. This is because I have found that whatever I am going through in life, particularly if it is something that I am finding difficult to deal with, when I turn to the Bible there are words of advice, comfort and support, healing and peace. So I now rely on God's love for me, as revealed in His Word, in my daily life. I don't rely on empty, meaningless rituals that enslave me to fear. It has taken me a long time to realise this, the better part of fifty years! But, as they say, it is never too late. Don't continue denying God in your life. When you respond to Him with a receptive attitude, a willingness to hear His Word and accept it, you will find that quiet sense of peace you seek.

Spend time reading and getting to know the Bible. If you are new to this, I recommend starting with the Psalms. Find a quiet time each day when you can be alone. You will soon find that you want to read and discover more and, in so doing, you are establishing and strengthening your personal relationship with God.

So, if you feel afraid and darkness threatens to overwhelm you, don't act from within a spirit of fear. Instead, turn to the Bible and...

Seek God's Help

> I sought the LORD, and he heard me, and delivered me from all my fears.
>
> Psalm 34:4

When you ask God for help, He does answer without fail. God is faithful. However, prayer is not some sort of magic talisman – a way of getting whatever you want! Your faith will very soon crumble away if you have this approach. Rather, when you pray, the answer you receive may not be what you expect, but it will be what you need!

> ...for your Father knoweth what things ye have need of, before ye ask him.
>
> Matthew 6:8

Prayer should be our first resort, not the last! In this way, by seeking God's help in prayer and relying on His Word, by focussing our mind and will on these, we choose the right path. We find our refuge, our strength in God's omnipotence, love and faithfulness, not in imprisoning, compulsive rituals. This is how you break out of the prison of fear, by having faith.

In God We Trust

Remember those words of healing I received from Psalm 46? This is how that Psalm begins:

> God is our refuge and strength, a very present help in trouble. Therefore will not we fear...
>
> Psalm 46:1-2

Conclusion

Many books have been written on the subject of fear, but this journey out of fear and towards God really happened to me. It can happen to you too. It's not a quick fix, though. This is a process of stages – breaking avoidance behaviours, discerning reality, looking outside yourself, stepping out with God and relying on His Word – you need to work through at your own pace, and it takes time. I can't tell you how long your journey will be or how long it will take, but I can promise that when you respond to God's love for you and trust in Him, you will be able to overcome OCD and anxiety.

Look what happened to me! When I asked God for help, those words, "Be still, and know that I am God," not only brought a very practical, immediate healing, but they have had a long-term effect as well. My life has been fundamentally changed: OCD no longer has a part in it. Little did I imagine, on that day, that I was being asked to confront something which had dominated and controlled me for so many years: fear. Little did I imagine that I would write a book about this experience in order to help others to be freed. This is the power of prayer: receiving what we need to move us further along on our journey towards God.

I still can't tell you why some of us are wired for anxiety and OCD, neither as yet can science. We simply have to recognise our propensity to anxiety. I know that I still tend to have an initial reaction of fear or anxiety when faced with unexpected events or potentially stressful situations that others take in their stride. The difference now is that I can very quickly quash that anxious or fearful response before it takes a hold on me. You accept the way you are and then you deal with it because you have the tools to do so now. When you find yourself reacting, stop! Reject that reaction, knowing that the fear you are feeling is unreal – an illusion. Turn to God:

> ...be not afraid ... for the LORD thy God is with thee withersoever thou goest.
>
> Joshua 1:9

Jesus said:

> *I am come that they might have life, and that they might have it more abundantly.*
>
> John 10:10

God wants us to live the best possible life and to live it to the fullest. When you are imprisoned by fear, addicted to it and enslaved by your compulsive rituals, you are not living a true life. You can be released.

God is with us. His love transforms lives, bringing light and hope where once there was fear and darkness. Step out with God and never look back!

Notes

For Further Study

Commentaries and Dictionary

- Dummelow, The Rev. J.R., Editor, The One Volume Bible Commentary, (Macmillan Publishing Co., Inc., New York, 1975)
- Easy English Commentary, (Various Contributors), See *www.easyenglish.info/bible-commentaries*
- An excellent Bible Dictionary can be found at *www.biblestudytools.com*

Part 1

CHAPTER 1

For further reading on the physiology of fear see Winston, Robert, Human Instinct, (Bantam Press, 2002).

For more on reaction to threat see Gilbert, Paul, The Compassionate Mind, (Constable, 2009).

Part 2

CHAPTER 5

For further reading see:
- Dean, Jeremy, "Why Thought Suppression is Counter-Productive", PsyBlog, May 2009.
- Gilbert, Paul, The Compassionate Mind, (Constable, 2009).

For more on self-acceptance see *theselfcompassionproject.com*

CHAPTER 6

For further reading see Jamison, Abbot Christopher, "Finding Happiness", (Weidenfeld and Nicolson, 2008).

when Mike told me that story years and years ago. That really put fear in me. We couldn't be so sure we believed him because he always made up stories when he was doing drugs and he lied so much. But that story he told left fear in me. What if he did, what was I suppose to do, was I suppose to tell that story to authorities, Was God going to punish me. Did I see that article on the web site to tell me God wanted me to do something. So my mind being tormented by God (Even though I knew God does not torment our minds, and that God was not the author of fear, and that he didn't give us a spirit of fear. I would try to figure out. It was torture. But now I am delivered from Fear. I know God is in Control. He loves me, and he is in control of my son whether it was true or not. I can rest in his safety, presence and know that he loves my Son and he's Got this.

I Love Him.